Stuck in Jelly

HarperCollinsChildren'sBooks

First published in India in 2022 by **HarperCollins Children's Books**
An imprint of HarperCollins *Publishers*
Building No 10, Tower A, 4th Floor,
DLF Cyber City, Phase II, Gurugram 122002
www.harpercollins.co.in

2 4 6 8 10 9 7 5 3 1

P-ISBN: 9789356293809
E-ISBN: 9789356293816

Typeset in CookieRunOTF 14 pt/24 by **Shamika Chaves**

Printed and bound by Nutech Print Services – India

HarperCollinsIn

Ricky

MUHAHAHA! You may know Pang as the group leader, but the true leader is me! You'll understand if you stick around! HAHAHA!

Oliver

What great weather we have today.
On a day like this, I just want to sit by the lake, eat cookies, and listen to some music.
So... Please don't take my cookies!

Shasha

I can make anything I put my mind to! So tell me what you need.
But don't go asking for too much, okay?

PANG

I like anything fun! Join me if you are feeling down.
PANG! A game of cricket will help you feel better!

Cash

Let's go play right now!!
It'll be fun! Quickly!
Cash has lots of great ideas!

Shasha has brought a basket
full of snacks to the cricket field.

The basket was filled with
clover-shaped cookies and one giant jelly bear.
"I made them especially for you guys!"
Shasha said.

Oliver really liked
the clover-shaped cookies.

"A four-leaf clover is a symbol of good luck!"
said Oliver.

Oliver's new hobby was
collecting four-leaf clovers
for good luck.

Cash played with the jelly bear
that Shasha had brought.
"It looks just like Oliver!" Cash said.

Just then a big bird swooped down and took away the jelly bear and dropped it into the forest.

"**Waaaa!**" cried Cash.

After an eventful snack time,
Oliver took a walk in the forest
to look for some four-leaf clovers.

While in the forest alone,
Oliver fell and got stuck on the jelly bear
that the bird had dropped.
He could not move.

When the break time was over, everyone gathered back
at the cricket field, except for Oliver.

They waited and waited, but Oliver did not show up.

"I'm a little worried," said Cash.

"Then we should go look for Oliver!" Shasha said.

While looking for Oliver in the forest,
the wind blew a couple of four-leaf clovers
towards Pang and his friends.

"Wasn't Oliver looking for them earlier?"
Cash said.

"Maybe we can find Oliver
if we go in that direction!"
said Pang.

Just then Cash smelt
the sweet smell of
his jelly bear in the forest.

Sniff
sniff

He followed the smell
and found Oliver
stuck to the jelly bear
on the ground.

Everyone tried their best to help Oliver. They cheered when Oliver tried to pull himself off the jelly bear.

Pang even tried hitting the jelly
with a bat but nothing seemed to work.

Soon the sun that was hiding in the clouds came out.
The sun melted the jelly bear, making it easier
for everyone to pull Oliver off the jelly.

"I'm finally free!" cheered Oliver.

Now that Oliver was free,
it was time to go back to cricket practice.
Cash looked back at
the melted jelly bear to say goodbye.

Cash accidentally fell on the jelly bear and got stuck.

"Save me!" Cash cried.

The **Cricket Pang** series is a set of picture books with charming stories based on lovable animal characters. The overall theme of the books is cricket, which besides being a very popular sport for children, also lends a unique flavour to this series. Children will love the main character, Pang, and his bunch of friends. Each book highlights important values through engaging stories and endearing characters. With their simple vocabulary and sentence structure, these books are perfect for early readers.

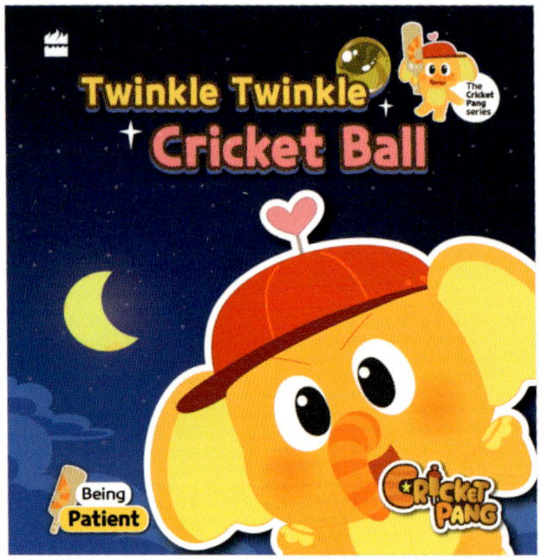

Being patient!

Being fair!

Being fun!

Being smart!

Follow our **YouTube Channel [CricketPang TV]** for more Cricket Pang content.
(QR code on the back cover)